A POCKET FULL OF LICORICE

Illustrated by Johnston & Cory

Apple Pie Alphabet

A is for apple pie.
B bit it.
C cut it.
D dealt it.
E enjoyed it.
F fingered it.
G got it.
H hid it.
I iced it.
J joined it.
K kept it.
L longed for it.
M made it.

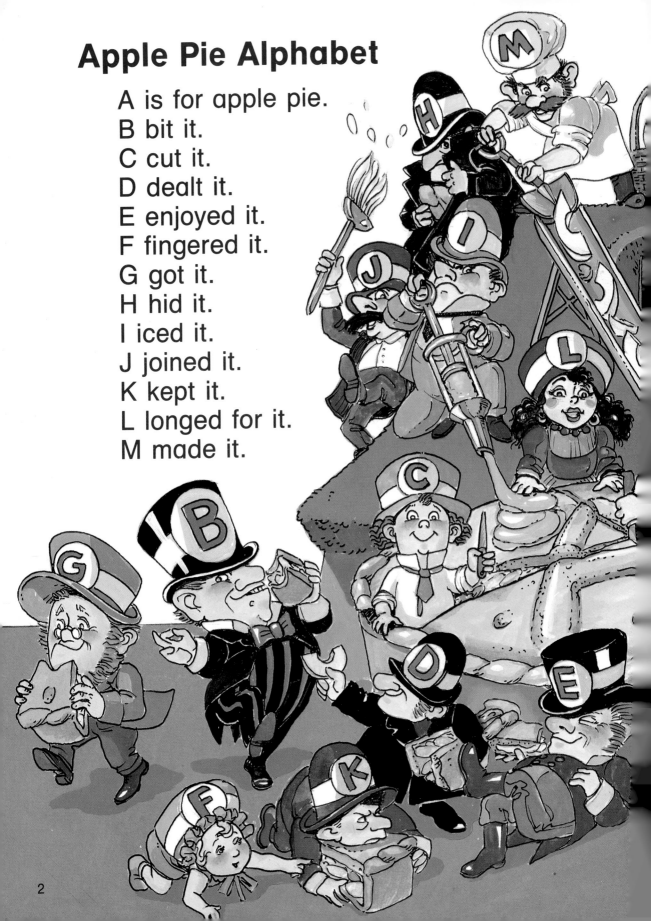

N needed it.
O opened it.
P peeped at it.
Q quartered it.
R ran for it.
S sliced it.
T took it.
U used it.
V viewed it.
W wanted it.
XYZ And now we've
made an apple pie.
All I want is
a piece to try.

Traditional

3

Polly Put the Kettle On

Polly put the kettle on,
Polly put the kettle on,
Polly put the kettle on,
    We'll all have tea.

Sukey take it off again,
Sukey take it off again,
Sukey take it off again,
    They've all gone away.

Traditional

K-K-K-Katy

K-K-K-Katy, beau-ti-ful Katy,
You're the only g-g-g-girl that I adore;
When the m-m-m-moon shines,
Over the cow-shed,
I'll be waiting at the k-k-k-kitchen door.

Geoffrey O'Hara

Go Tell Aunt Rhody

Go tell Aunt Rhody,
Go tell Aunt Rhody,
Go tell Aunt Rhody,
The old gray goose is dead.

The one she was saving,
The one she was saving,
The one she was saving,
To make a feather bed.

The old gander is mourning,
The old gander is mourning,
The old gander is mourning,
Because his wife is dead.

The little goslings are weeping,
The little goslings are weeping,
The little goslings are weeping,
Because their mama's dead.

The whole family's weeping,
The whole family's weeping,
The whole family's weeping,
Because their mama's dead.   American Folk Song

7

The Bunny

There was a little bunny.
He lived in a wood.
He waggled his ears
    as a little bunny should.

He hopped by a squirrel.
He hopped by a tree.
He hopped by a duck,
    and he hopped by me.

He stared at the squirrel.
He stared at the tree.
He stared at the duck,
    but he made a face at me!

Eleanore Underwood

The Rabbit

Hip hop hoppity. Hip hop hoppity.
The rabbit leaps. The rabbit bounds.
His ears are long and soft and floppity.
They let him hear the slightest sounds.

Jack Prelutsky

Jump, Jump

Jump, jump,
Jump to the sun.
Jump, jump,
Jumping is fun.

Jump, jump,
Jump to the stars.
Jump, jump,
Jump back to Mars.

Jump, jump,
Jump to the moon.
Jump, jump,
Jump back soon.

Helen Crane

Here Am I

Here am I,
    Little Jumping Joan.
When nobody's with me,
    I'm all alone.

Traditional

11

Engine, Engine

Engine, engine number nine,
Running down Chicago line,
Shine my shoes with turpentine,
Engine, engine number nine.

Miss Quiss

Miss Quiss! Look at this!
A pocket full of licorice!
You may have some
If you wish,
But ev'ry stick will cost you a kiss!

Clyde Watson

Queenie

Queenie's strong and Queenie's tall.
You should see her bat a ball,
Ride a bike, or climb a wall.
(Queenie's not her name at all.)

Queenie's nimble, Queenie's quick.
You should see her throw a stick,
Watch her saw a board that's thick,
See her do her tumbling trick.

Queenie's not afraid, like me,
Of snakes or climbing up a tree.
(I think that's why the boys agree,
Queenie's what her name should be.)

Leland B. Jacobs

Jack and Jill

Jack and Jill
Went up the hill,
To fetch a pail of water;
Jack fell down,
And broke his crown,
And Jill came tumbling after.

Then up Jack got,
And home did trot,
As fast as he could caper;
To old Dame Dob,
Who patched his nob
With vinegar and brown paper.

Traditional

My Father's Valentine

I'm working on a valentine,
my very special own design,
a heart to give my dad tonight
(it's quite a chore to get it right).

The first time that I cut it out,
one side was thin, the other stout,
and so I tried to fix it, but
I made an error when I cut.

Jack Prelutsky

Roses Are Red

Roses are red,
violets are blue,
Sugar is sweet,
and so are you.

A Delicious Cake

Mix the batter,
Stir the batter,
Shake some flour in.
Mix the batter,
Stir the batter,
Place it in a tin.

Traditional

18

Whistle

I want to learn to whistle,
I've always wanted to;
I fix my mouth to do it, but
The whistle won't come through.

Unknown

I Had a Cat

I had a cat and the cat pleased me,
I fed my cat by yonder tree;
  Cat goes *fiddle-i-fee*.

I had a hen and the hen pleased me,
I fed my hen by yonder tree;
  Hen goes *chimmy-chuck, chimmy-chuck,*
  Cat goes *fiddle-i-fee*.

Traditional

The Yak

Yickity-yackity, yickity-yak,
the yak has a scriffily, scraffily back;
some yaks are brown yaks
and some yaks are black,
yickity-yackity, yickity-yak.

Jack Prelutsky

Fuzzy Wuzzy

Fuzzy Wuzzy was a bear.
Fuzzy Wuzzy had no hair.
Fuzzy Wuzzy wasn't fuzzy,
Was he?

Traditional

My Zipper Suit

My zipper suit is bunny-brown —
The top zips up, the legs zip down.
I wear it every day.
My daddy brought it out from town.
Zip it up, and zip it down,
And hurry out to play.

Mary Louise Allen

I Like It When It's Mizzly

I like it when it's mizzly
and just a little drizzly
so everything looks far away
and make-believe and frizzly.

Aileen Fisher

Night is Come

Night is come,
  Nobody is out;
Beetles hum
  Round about.

Children snore
  Now in bed;
Nothing more
  Need be said.

Sir Henry Newbolt